Literacy
Activity Book

Year 1 Term 1

Louis Fidge

EDUCATIONAL

Every effort has been made to trace copyright holders and to obtain their permission for the use of copyright material. The authors and publishers would gladly receive information enabling them to rectify any error or omission in subsequent editions.

Acknowledgements

Extract from *Something Special* by Nicola Moon, first published in the UK by Orchard Books in 1995, a division of The Watts Publishing Group Limited, 96 Leonard Street, London EC2A 4XD.

When I Get Up in the Morning by Clive Webster, taken from *First Verses* (OUP). Used with the kind permission of the author.

Extract from *Frog and Toad are Friends* by Arnold Lobel © 1971, 1972 Arnold Lobel. First published in Great Britain by World's Work Ltd and Mammoth and used with permission of Egmont Children's Books Limited, London.

First published 2000

Letts Educational
9–15 Aldine Street, London W12 8AW
Tel: 020 8740 2270   Fax: 020 8740 2280

Text © Louis Fidge

Designed by Gecko Limited, Bicester, Oxon
Produced by Ken Vail Graphic Design, Cambridge

Colour reproduction by PDQ, Bungay, Suffolk

Illustrated by Phil Burrows, Rob Englebright, Sarah Geeves, Graham-Cameron Illustration (Tamsin Cook, Bridget Dowty and Kirsty Wilson), Simon Girling & Associates (Carol Daniel, Mimi Everett and Piers Harper) and Tim Oliver.

British Library Cataloguing-in-Publication Data
A CIP record for this book is available from the British Library

ISBN 1 84085 387 5

Printed in Spain by Mateu Cromo

Letts Educational, a division of Granada Learning Ltd. Part of the Granada Media Group.

Introduction

The Year 1 Literacy Textbooks:

- support the teaching of the Literacy Hour
- are best used along with the *Year 1 Poster Packs* and *Teacher's Notes* which provide more detailed suggestions for development activities
- help meet the majority of the objectives of the National Literacy Strategy Framework (when used in conjunction with the *Year 1 Poster Pack* and *Teacher's Notes*)
- are divided into three books, each containing one term's work
- contain ten units per term (equivalent to one unit a week)

- contain one Writing Focus unit each term to support compositional writing
- provide coverage of a wide range of writing, both fiction and non-fiction, as identified in the National Literacy Strategy Framework
- assume an adult (a teacher, parent or classroom assistant) will be supporting the children, reading to and with them, and mediating the tasks
- assume much of the work will be done orally, with written responses expected only as and when pupils have sufficient competence to record them.

Unit number

Key teaching points

Text for reading and discussion

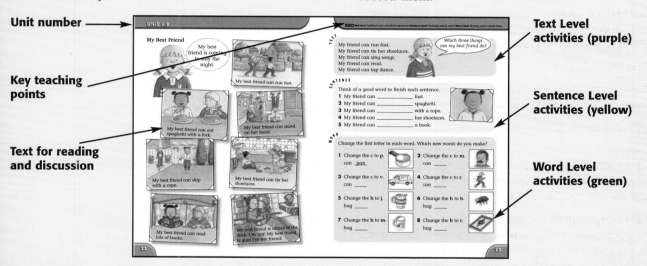

Text Level activities (purple)

Sentence Level activities (yellow)

Word Level activities (green)

Writing Focus unit:

- appears on pages 26–29
- develops aspects of work covered in preceding ten units
- supports work on compositional writing
- contains support and suggestions for the teaching of different essential writing skills
- assumes much work will be done orally through discussion
- assumes that an adult will act as a scribe, helping children record their ideas for much of the time, and that children will only be expected to record as their developing writing competencies allow.

Phonic Check-up:

- appears on pages 30–31
- reviews the phonic work covered in the preceding ten units
- may be used to provide a review of progress or as further practice in areas of concern.

High Frequency Word List:

- appears on page 32
- contains words that frequently appear in children's reading and writing
- may be used to help children to recognise these words on sight and spell them correctly
- provides an easily accessible resource for spelling and reading activities and a ready reference section.

Text Level	Sentence Level	Word Level
• Reading and locating parts of text	Predicting missing words	The alphabet
• Reading and locating parts of text	Predicting missing words	Rhyming patterns
• Reading and locating parts of text	Reordering words	Initial letter sounds in c-v-c words
• Reading and using captions/labels	Expecting a text to make sense	Final letter sounds in c-v-c words
• Reading and locating parts of text	Using capital letters and full stops	Blending c-v-c words
• Recounting main points	Using capital letters and full stops	Phonemes
• Reading and locating parts of text	Recognising speech	Blending phonemes
• Reading and understanding features of rhyme	Predicting missing words	Rhyming patterns
• Relating to own and other's experience	Predicting missing words	Rhyming patterns/ initial letters
• Relating stories/reading lists	Expecting a text to make sense	Medial letter sounds

Writing Focus — *Writing from personal experience; Writing a number rhyme; Writing a patterned story; Writing instructions; Writing lists*

Phonic Check-up — *Review of Word Level skills covered in Units 1.1–1.10*

Year 1, Term 1

CONTENTS

My Holiday

I went on a plane.

I stayed in a caravan.

I ate an ice cream.

I played in a rock pool.

I made a sandcastle.

I got wet!

EXT

1 What did the girl go on?

2 Where did the girl stay?

3 What did the girl eat?

4 Where did the girl play?

5 What did the girl make?

6 What happened to the girl?

NTENCE

Choose the best word for each sentence.

1 I _____ (stayed/went) on a plane.

2 I _____ (stayed/played) in a caravan.

3 I _____ (played/ate) an ice cream.

4 I _____ (ate/played) in a rock pool.

5 I _____ (ate/made) a sandcastle.

RD

1 Which letters are missing?

a b __ d e f __ h i __ k l __ n o __ q r s __ u v w __ y __

2 Which letters are missing?

A __ C D __ F G __ I J __ L M __ O P __ R __
T U __ W X __ Z

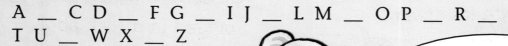

Can you say the
sound of each letter?
Do you know the name of
each letter?

7

Number One, Stick Out Your Tongue

Number one, stick out your tongue.
Number two, take off your shoe.
Number three, bend your knee.
Number four, open the door.
Number five, learn to jive.
Number six, pick up sticks.
Number seven, point to heaven.
Number eight, shut the gate.
Number nine, touch your spine.
Number ten, do it again!

TEXT

What must you do with:

1 your tongue?
2 the door?
3 your spine?
4 your shoe?
5 the sticks?

SENTENCE

Copy and fill in the missing words.

1 Number one, stick out your _____.
2 Number two, take off your _____.
3 Number three, bend your _____.
4 Number four, open the _____.
5 Number five, learn to _____.

WORD

Match up the pairs of words that rhyme.

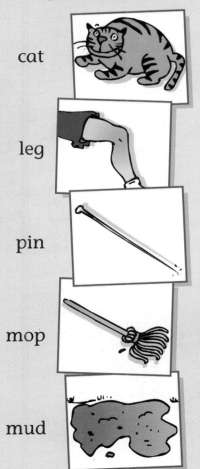

cat

leg

pin

mop

mud

bin

top

mat

bud

peg

Samir's Busy Week

On Monday Samir was an astronaut.

On Tuesday Samir was a deep sea diver.

On Wednesday Samir was a detective.

On Thursday Samir was a doctor.

On Friday Samir was a pop singer.

On Saturday Samir was a vet.

On Sunday Samir had a rest.

TEXT

1 What was Samir on Monday?

2 What was Samir on Saturday?

3 What was Samir on Wednesday?

4 What was Samir on Friday?

5 What was Samir on Tuesday?

SENTENCE

The words below have got muddled. Put the words in the correct order.

1 Wednesday Samir was on a detective

2 Saturday Samir was on a vet

3 Monday Samir was on an astronaut

4 Thursday Samir was on a doctor

5 Sunday Samir had a rest on

WORD

Choose the correct letter to begin each word.

1 f   m

__an

2 l   p
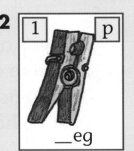
__eg

3 h   s

__it

4 b   r
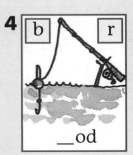
__od

5 t   p

__ub

6 d   j

__og

7 f   s
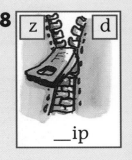
__un

8 z   d
__ip

My Body

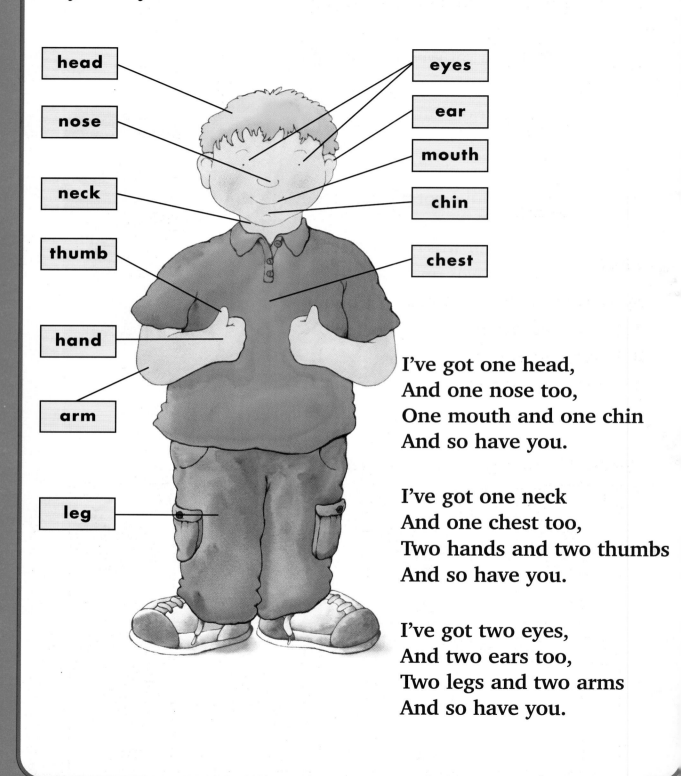

head

nose

neck

thumb

hand

arm

leg

eyes

ear

mouth

chin

chest

I've got one head,
And one nose too,
One mouth and one chin
And so have you.

I've got one neck
And one chest too,
Two hands and two thumbs
And so have you.

I've got two eyes,
And two ears too,
Two legs and two arms
And so have you.

TEXT

Copy this picture and label it correctly.

hair

eye

ear

nose

mouth

chin

SENTENCE

Make each sentence correct.

1 I have two heads.
2 I have four eyes.
3 I have two necks.
4 I have three legs.
5 I have two noses.
6 I have five thumbs.

WORD

Choose the correct letter to end each word.

1 f   g
lo__

2 n   p

pa—

3 x   s

si__

4 c   d
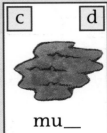
mu__

5 t   p

ne__

6 p   j

cu__

7 f   m

ja__

8 z   b

so__

Wendy Wanted to Whistle

Wendy tried to whistle in the bath. She blew and blew until her cheeks got tired – but it was no good!

Wendy tried to whistle in bed. She blew and blew until she made herself dizzy – but it was no good!

Wendy tried to whistle in the kitchen. She blew and blew until her tea got cold – but it was no good!

Wendy tried to whistle in the swimming pool. She blew and blew until she swallowed a mouthful of water – but it was no good!

Wendy tried to whistle at school. She blew and blew – and out came a squeaky whistle!

Wendy was so pleased that she whistled all the way home.

TEXT

1 Where was Wendy when her cheeks got tired?

2 Where was Wendy when she made herself dizzy?

3 Where was Wendy when her tea got cold?

4 Where was Wendy when she swallowed some water?

5 Where was Wendy when she made a squeaky whistle?

SENTENCE

Begin each sentence with a capital letter and end it with a full stop.

1 i can run

2 i can hop

3 i can skip

4 i can jump

5 wendy can whistle

6 i can sing

WORD

Look at these word sums. Which words can you make?

1    p + a + t

2    b + e + g

3    m + i + x

4   h + o + p

5    r + u + n

6    s + i + t

How to Make a Sock Snake

What you need:

| an old sock | some coloured material | scissors | glue |

What you do:

1.

Cut out the tongue
for your snake.

2.

Cut out two eyes.

3.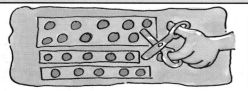

Cut out some stripes.

4.

Stick the tongue, eyes and
stripes onto the sock.

5. Make your snake come alive.

TEXT

Put these sentences in the right order.

◆ Cut out some stripes.

◆ Stick the tongue, eyes and stripes onto the sock.

◆ Cut out the tongue for your snake.

◆ Make your snake come alive.

◆ Cut out two eyes.

SENTENCE

Copy these sentences. Begin each one with a capital letter and end it with a full stop.

1 you need an old sock

2 you need some glue

3 you need some material

4 you need some scissors

5 now you can make a snake

WORD

Look at the word sums. Which words can you make?

1  c + u + t   **2**  h + u + t

3  p + e + n   **4**  h + e + n

5  w + a + g   **6**  b + a + g

7  m + o + p   **8**  h + o + p

17

Something Special

At school on Thursday Charlie was very excited.

"I'm bringing something really special to show tomorrow," he said.

At last it was Friday.

"Charlie has something special to show us this morning," said Mrs Brown.

"This is my baby sister," said Charlie proudly. "She's called Sally and she's six weeks old. She smiles at me and she's very special."

"She looks like you," said Peter.

"When will she be big enough to play football?" said Daniel.

"I wish I had a baby sister," said Lu Mei.

"She isn't smiling at me," said Steven.

"She only smiles at me," said Charlie, "because I'm her brother."

From Something Special *by Nicola Moon*

TEXT

1 What is the name of the teacher?

2 When did Charlie take the baby into school?

3 What is the name of the baby?

4 Is the baby a boy or a girl?

5 How old is the baby?

SENTENCE

What did each person say?

1 Mrs Brown

2 Peter

3 Daniel

4 Lu Mei

5 Steven

WORD

Make some words using these letter bricks.

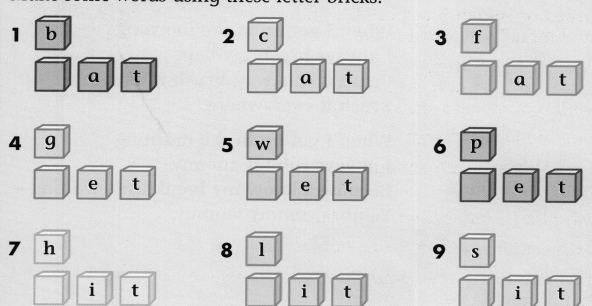

1 b ☐ a t

2 c ☐ a t

3 f ☐ a t

4 g ☐ e t

5 w ☐ e t

6 p ☐ e t

7 h ☐ i t

8 l ☐ i t

9 s ☐ i t

When I Get Up in the Morning

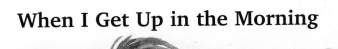
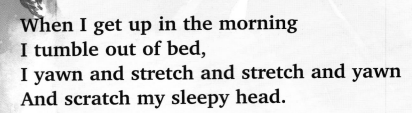

When I get up in the morning
I tumble out of bed,
I yawn and stretch and stretch and yawn
And scratch my sleepy head.

When I get up in the morning
I always wash my face,
And splash and splash the soapy water
All around the place.

When I get up in the morning
I always clean my teeth,
Front and back and back and front
On top and underneath.

When I get up in the morning
I always brush my hair,
Brush it this way, brush it that,
Brush it everywhere.

When I get up in the morning
I always rub my tummy,
Because I know my breakfast's waiting –
Yummy yummy yummy.

When I Get Up in the Morning by Clive Webster from First Verses

TEXT

1 What is the poem called?
2 How many verses are there in the poem?
3 What does each verse start with?
4 How many lines are in each verse?
5 Which word rhymes with 'bed'?

SENTENCE

Find the missing words.
1 I tumble out of _____.
2 I always wash my _____.
3 I always clean my _____.
4 I always brush my _____.
5 I always rub my _____.

WORD

1 Find the pairs of rhyming words on the duvet.

bed cot fix mix red fun bun map hot tap

2 Think of a word that rhymes with:
   a) bag b) beg c) big
   d) bug e) bog

21

My Best Friend

My best friend is coming to stay the night.

My best friend can run fast.

My best friend can eat spaghetti with a fork.

My best friend can stand on her head.

My best friend can skip with a rope.

My best friend can tie her shoelaces.

My best friend can read lots of books.

My best friend is afraid of the dark. I'm not! My best friend is glad I'm her friend!

TEXT

My friend can run fast.
My friend can tie her shoelaces.
My friend can sing songs.
My friend can read.
My friend can tap dance.

Which three things can my best friend do?

SENTENCE

Think of a good word to finish each sentence.

1 My friend can _____ fast.

2 My friend can _____ spaghetti.

3 My friend can _____ with a rope.

4 My friend can _____ her shoelaces.

5 My friend can _____ a book.

WORD

Change the first letter in each word. Which new words do you make?

1 Change the **c** to **p**.
can __pan__

2 Change the **c** to **m**.
can _____

3 Change the **c** to **v**.
can _____

4 Change the **c** to **r**.
can _____

5 Change the **h** to **j**.
hug _____

6 Change the **h** to **b**.
hug _____

7 Change the **h** to **m**.
hug _____

8 Change the **h** to **r**.
hug _____
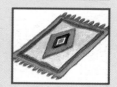

23

Toad's List

One day Toad made a list of all the things he had to do so he would remember them.

A list of things to do today
Wake up
Eat Breakfast
Get Dressed
Go to Frog's House
Take walk with Frog
Eat lunch
Take nap
Play games with Frog
Eat Supper
Go to Sleep

"There," said Toad. "Now my day is all written down."

He got out of bed and had something to eat.

Then Toad crossed out:

~~Eat Breakfast~~

From Frog and Toad Together *(slightly adapted)*
by Arnold Lobel

TEXT

1 Why did Toad make a list?

2 What is the first thing on his list?

3 What is the second thing on his list?

4 What is the last thing on his list?

5 Why did Toad cross something out on his list?

SENTENCE

I have got some things muddled up. Can you correct them for me?

- Eat to Frog's house
- Take Breakfast
- Go games with Frog
- Play to Sleep
- Go a walk with Frog

WORD

Choose the correct letter for the middle of each word.

1 | u | a |
c_p

2 | i | a |
b_g

3 | e | u |
b_d

4 | i | e |
p__n

5 | i | a |
w_g

6 | o | u |
h_p

7 | i | o |
f_x

8 | u | a |
b_n

1. Writing from personal experience

1 Write about a special event.

> Read about my holiday in Unit 1.1 again. I made my story into my own book!

◆ Choose something special that has happened to you. It may have been:
  – a special birthday or celebration
  – a special holiday
  – somewhere special you have visited.

◆ Draw some pictures.

◆ Write a sentence under each picture.

◆ Make your own book!

2 Write about a special friend.

> Read about my special friend in Unit 1.9.

◆ Write about some things **your** best friend can do.

◆ Draw a picture for each thing. Do it like this.

My best friend knows how to skip.

2. Writing a number rhyme

1 Read Unit 1.2 again.

Finish this number rhyme in your own words.

Number one, I play in the sun.

Number two, I paint my face <u>blue</u> .

Number three, I climb a _____ .

Number four, I slam the _____ .

Number _____ , I swim and dive.

Number six, I build with _____ .

Number _____ , I go to Devon.

Number _____ , I slide and skate.

Number nine, I'm feeling _____ .

Number ten, let's start again!

DEVON

Do you know any other number rhymes?
Try and make up one of your own.

3. Writing a patterned story

1 Read Unit 1.3 again.

Make up something **amazing** that you did each day of the week.
Do it like this:

On Monday I had dinner with a dragon.

On Tuesday I flew to the moon.

On Wednesday I chased a giant.

On Thursday I climbed a mountain.

On Friday I played with a crocodile.

On Saturday I had tea with the Queen.

On Sunday I had a rest.

4. Writing instructions

1 Look at the instructions in Unit 1.6 again.

Here is a list of the things I needed to grow some mustard and cress seeds.

| egg shell | soil | seeds | water |

◆ Use the pictures below to help you make up some simple instructions.
Do it like this:

1. First I put some soil into an egg shell.

1   **2**   **3**   **4**

5. Writing lists

1 Read Unit 1.10 again.

• bucket and spade
• sunglasses
• camera
• shorts
• sun hat
• ball

*Here is a list of some things I took when I went on holiday.
Now make your own list.*

Phonic Check-up

1 Which letters are missing?

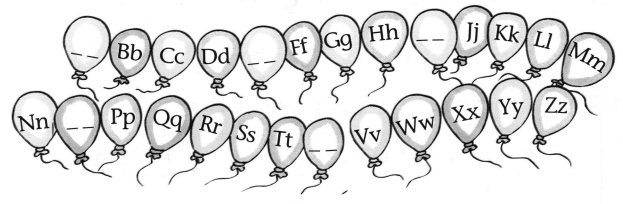

2 Find the pairs of rhyming words.

a) bad   mad   tip

b) hen   log   men

c) cup   sit   bit

d) box   rag   fox

e) gum   hum   net

f) din   den   pin

3 Choose the correct letter to begin each word.

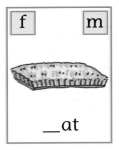

f   m

__at

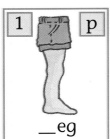

l   p

__eg

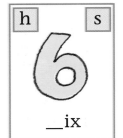

h   s

__ix

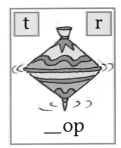

t   r

__op

4 Choose the correct letter to end each word.

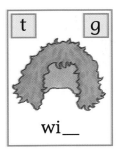

t   g

wi__

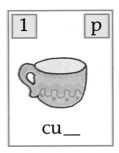

l   p

cu__

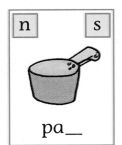

n   s

pa__

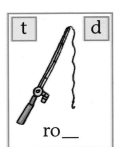

t   d

ro__

5 Make some more words. Draw a picture for each word.

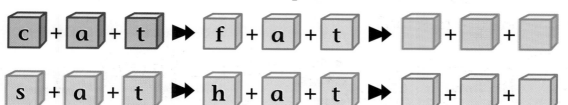

c + a + t ▶ f + a + t ▶ ☐ + ☐ + ☐

s + a + t ▶ h + a + t ▶ ☐ + ☐ + ☐

6 Make the jigsaw words. Draw a picture for each word.

d og   f og   l og

7 Make the words.
Match each word to the correct picture.

h + e + n =

l + i + d =

m + o + p =

t + u + b =

8 Choose the correct letter for the middle of each word.

a   u

c__p

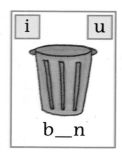

i   u

b__n

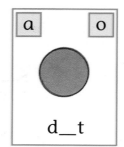

a   o

d__t

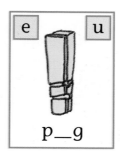

e   u

p__g

High Frequency Word List

about
after
again
an
another
as

back
ball
be
because
bed
been
boy
brother
but
by

call(ed)
came
can't
could

did
do
don't
door
down

first
from

girl
good
got

had
half
has
have
help
her
here
him

his
home
house
how

if

jump
just

last
laugh
little
live(d)
love

made
make
man
many
may
more
much
must

name
new
next
night
not
now

off
old
once
one
or
our
out
over

people
pull
push
put

ran

saw
school
seen
should
sister
so
some

take
than
that
their
them
then
there
these
three
time
too
took
tree
two

us

very

want
water
way
were
what
when
where
who
will
with
would

your

Days of the week:
Monday
Tuesday
Wednesday
Thursday
Friday
Saturday
Sunday

Months:
January
February
March
April
May
June
July
August
September
October
November
December

Colours:
black
blue
brown
green
pink
orange
purple
red
white
yellow

Numbers to twenty:
one
two
three
four
five
six
seven
eight
nine
ten
eleven
twelve
thirteen
fourteen
fifteen
sixteen
seventeen
eighteen
nineteen
twenty